# Silent Nights: A Meditative Christmas coloring book for adults relaxation

Clara Noel

# Introduction to Silent Nights: A Meditative Christmas

The holiday season brings twinkling lights, joyful gatherings, and cherished traditions. Yet it also carries busyness, expectations, and fatigue. *Silent Nights: A Meditative Christmas* is an invitation to pause — to find stillness amid the swirl of activity. Coloring itself is a meditative act, a quiet rhythm of shape and shade that pulls us gently into the present moment.

Here, intricate mandalas echo the quiet order of snowflakes, while winter foliage and Christmas symbols remind us of peace, generosity, and renewal. As you color, allow each page to become more than art. Let it be an act of care — for your mind, your breath, your body, your spirit.

You don't need to finish quickly. There's no right or wrong. Each stroke of color is an arrival into calm. Each page holds a prompt or affirmation to guide you deeper into presence. Some invite you to breathe with intention. Others encourage reflection. Others simply whisper reassurance that all is well, even in winter's hush.

This is your season of stillness. Your Silent Night. May these pages help you rest, soften, and return to yourself.

# Festive Coloring Tips for a Meditative Christmas

Coloring is not about skill — it's about presence. Still, having a few creative ideas can help you enjoy the process more deeply. Here are some festive and calming approaches to try as you bring these pages to life:

### 1. Embrace the Palette of Winter

• Use **cool tones** — icy blues, soft grays, snowy whites — to capture stillness and serenity.

• Add touches of **silver or metallic pens** to mimic frost and shimmer.

• For warmth, blend **deep reds, forest greens, and golds**, evoking Christmas hearths and candlelight.

### 2. Layer Like Snow

Build your colors in soft layers, just as snow gathers flake by flake. Begin with light strokes, then gradually deepen. This not only looks beautiful but also slows your pace, keeping your movements mindful.

### 3. Mindful Shading

While filling a section, notice how your hand moves. Breathe with each stroke. Try shading from dark to light, imagining the glow of a candle spreading outward.

### 4. Celebrate Contrast

Christmas is full of opposites — dark nights and bright lights, frosty air and warm cocoa. Use **contrasting colors** (like deep indigo against golden yellow) to mirror that balance.

### 5. Add Sparkle & Shine

Experiment with gel pens, metallic markers, or even a touch of glitter to bring magic to stars, ornaments, or snowflakes. Small highlights create a festive glow.

### 6. Nature-Inspired Colors

Look to the outdoors for guidance:

- Evergreen needles = deep greens
- Holly berries = rich red
- Pinecones = warm browns
- Winter skies = pale grays and blues

Let nature's palette guide your hand.

### 7. Affirmation Coloring

Pair an affirmation with your page. For example, as you color snowflakes, repeat: *"I choose peace over perfection."*Allow the words to flow with the colors, weaving calm into the image.

### 8. Holiday Music Companion

Play soft Christmas instrumentals or carols while you color. Match your color flow to the rhythm of the music, letting the experience become both visual and auditory meditation.

**9. Color with Intention**

Before starting, choose a word — *peace, light, gratitude, joy*. Select colors that feel like that word to you. As you fill the page, you'll see your intention come to life in color.

**10. Celebrate the Imperfect**

Just as no snowflake is the same, your pages don't need to be perfect. Let mistakes be part of the art. The process is the gift — not the outcome.

✨ Tip: Keep a favorite set of pencils, pens, or markers just for this book. Over time, opening them will feel like opening a box of calm.

# Breathing & Relaxation Prompts

### 1. Snowflake Breath

Close your eyes and imagine a delicate snowflake drifting from the sky. As it falls, take a slow breath in. Feel the cool air filling your lungs, crisp and pure. As the snowflake settles on the earth, exhale gently, releasing tension from your shoulders and chest.

Repeat this three times. Each inhale, notice the freshness. Each exhale, let your body soften, like the ground receiving snow. Allow yourself to become part of winter's hush.

### 2. Candle Flame Focus

Visualize a single candle flickering in the dark. Watch its steady glow. As you breathe in, imagine drawing that light into your heart. As you exhale, imagine releasing the chaos of the season — the lists, the rush, the pressure.

Keep breathing with the flame. Your inhale keeps it bright. Your exhale clears the air around it. Soon, you'll feel as steady as the flame itself: soft, warm, unwavering.

### 3. Box of Gift Breath

Think of your breath as a gift you are unwrapping. Breathe in slowly for four counts — this is the gift opening. Hold the breath for four counts — this is the pause of anticipation. Exhale for four counts — this is the joy of receiving. Rest for four counts — this is the gratitude.

Repeat four cycles, imagining you are wrapping yourself in calm. A gift you give yourself, over and over.

**4. Evergreen Grounding**

Picture yourself as an evergreen tree in winter. With each inhale, feel nourishment rising through your roots. With each exhale, release what no longer serves you into the soil below.

As you color, notice the connection between your hand, the page, and the earth beneath. Like the evergreen, you are steady, resilient, and deeply rooted, even in the coldest season.

# Meditative Reflections

### The Quiet of Snow

Snow transforms the world. Streets hush, branches bend, and the earth takes on a soft blanket of stillness. In these moments, life slows, reminding us that it is natural to pause. Just as snow insists the land must rest, so too may you. Coloring this page, imagine yourself wrapped in snow's quiet.

### The Glow of Lights

Lights strung across rooftops and trees remind us that even in the darkest nights, beauty can shine. Notice how light needs darkness to be seen. Your calm shines brightest when you allow space for rest. As you color glowing stars or candles, let each spark remind you of your own inner glow.

### The Evergreen Promise

While other trees shed their leaves, evergreens stay green all winter long. They remind us that strength and life endure, even when the world looks bare. As you shade in pine branches or holly leaves, reflect on the steady strength within you that survives every season.

### Silent Night, Holy Night

True silence is a gift. It is in the pause between notes, the stillness before dawn, the breath that steadies the soul. As you color mandalas inspired by this carol, imagine yourself resting in sacred quiet. In this silence, you are whole. In this stillness, you are free.

## Closing Reflection

As you reach the final pages, take a deep breath. Let your shoulders soften. Notice the colors you've brought to life, the patterns you've filled with care. This journey is not about perfection, but presence.

Stillness is always available to you. When the holidays feel heavy, return to a single breath, a gentle affirmation, or the quiet rhythm of coloring. These are your tools of calm — simple, steady, always near.

You are enough, just as you are. You are light in the darkness. You are warmth in the cold.

May your nights be silent, your heart be light, and your spirit be renewed.

- ***I bring happiness and positivity to those I encounter.***
- ***I am a symbol of unity and love during Christmas.***
- ***Christmas is a time for healing and forgiveness.***
- ***I am open to the magic and miracles of the season.***
- ***I embrace the spirit of togetherness and love.***
- ***I share the gift of laughter and smiles with others.***
- ***I am a source of comfort and solace for those in need.***

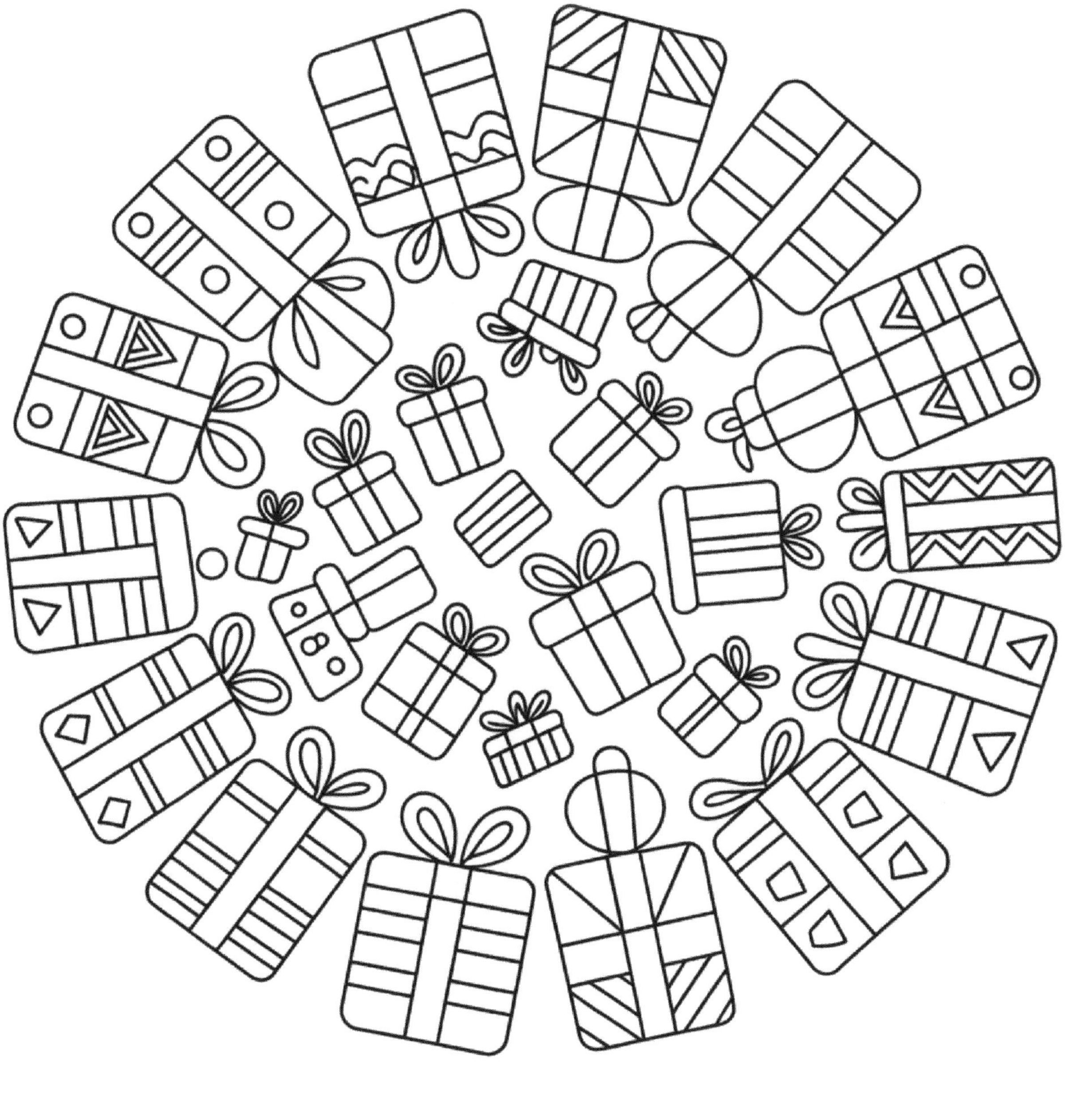

- *The holiday season fills me with hope, serenity, and joy.*
- *I am thankful for the gift of life, love, and family at Christmas.*
- *I am a shining star, lighting up the world with my positivity.*
- *I appreciate the beauty and tranquility of the snowfall.*
- *I find joy in the act of giving, making hearts merry and bright.*
- *I am grateful for the abundance, peace, and prosperity of the season.*
- *I am open to receiving and sharing love, kindness, and goodwill.*

- *I am grateful for the abundance, peace, and prosperity of the season.*
- *I am open to receiving and sharing love, kindness, and goodwill.*
- *Christmas is a time for celebration, love, and merriment.*
- *I am a vessel of peace, harmony, and joy during Christmas.*
- *I create a welcoming, cozy atmosphere in my home and heart.*

- ***I create a welcoming, cozy atmosphere in my home and heart.***
- ***I am surrounded by the love and laughter of cherished family and friends.***
- ***I am a source of inspiration, positivity, and delight for others.***
- ***I find delight in the enchanting music and carols of Christmas.***
- ***I am thankful for the magic, wonder, and enchantment of the season.***
- ***I generously share my blessings and abundance with those in need.***

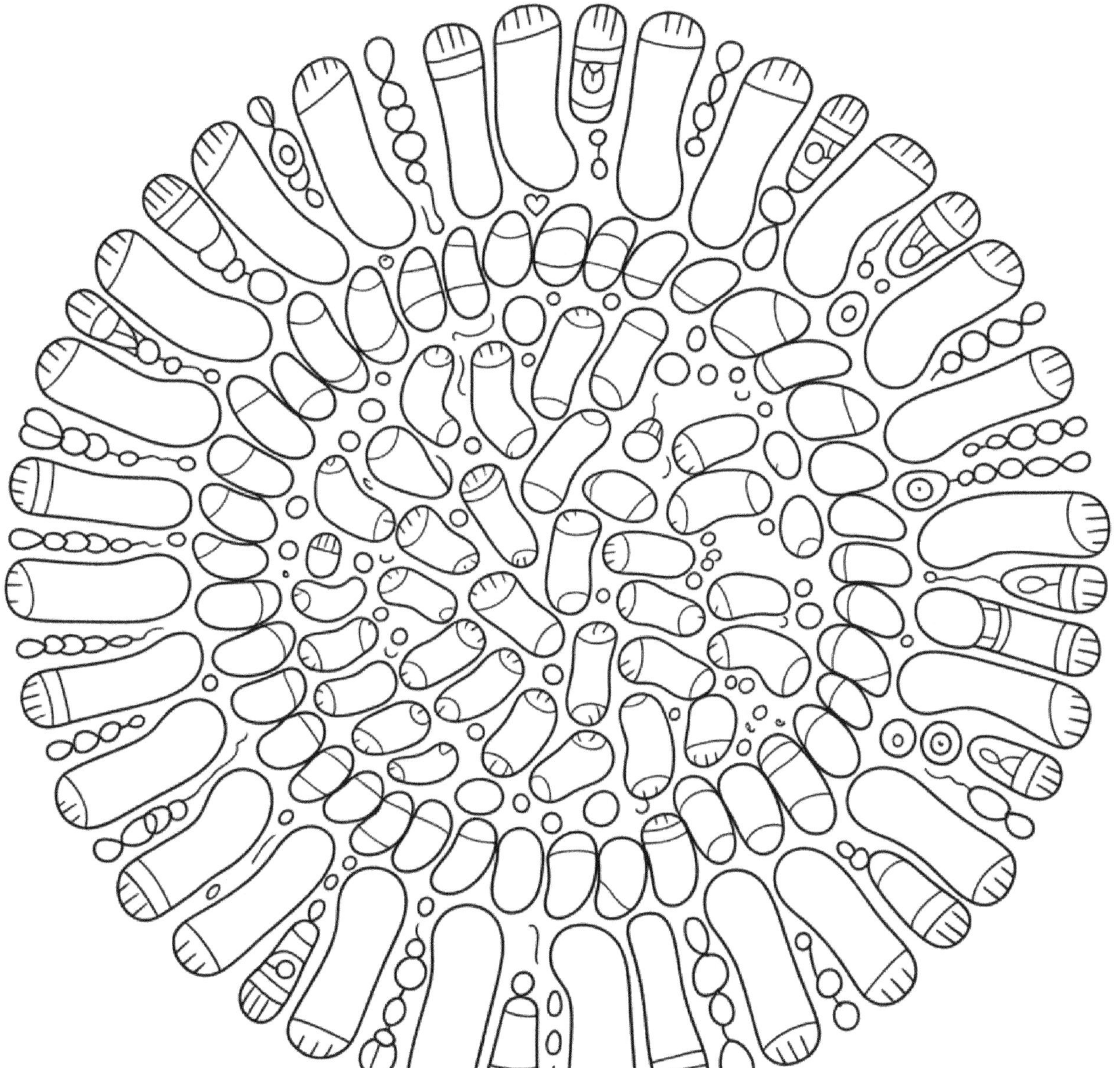

- ***I am a vessel of peace, harmony, and joy during Christmas.***
- ***I create a welcoming, cozy atmosphere in my home and heart.***
- ***I am surrounded by the love and laughter of cherished family and friends.***
- ***I am a source of inspiration, positivity, and delight for others.***
- ***I find delight in the enchanting music and carols of Christmas.***
- ***I am thankful for the magic, wonder, and enchantment of the season.***

- *I find delight in the enchanting music and carols of Christmas.*
- *I am thankful for the magic, wonder, and enchantment of the season.*
- *I generously share my blessings and abundance with those in need.*
- *I am open to the joy of giving and receiving, spreading love and joy.*
- *Christmas is a time for renewal, grace, and new beginnings.*
- *I cherish the love, camaraderie, and the bonds of friendship.*

www.ingramcontent.com/pod-product-compliance
Lightning Source LLC
LaVergne TN
LVHW070522061126
851857LV00023B/2131
* 9 7 8 3 9 2 9 4 7 0 5 5 0 *